MW00954127

Copyright 2018 by Sandra A. Roberts

All rights reserved. This book or any portion thereof may
not be reproduced or used in any manner whatsoever without
the express written permission of the publisher except for
the use of brief quotations in a book review.

Books in Our Image
www.booksinourimage.com

Book Design and Layout by Cassandra Bowen, Uzuri Designs
www.uzuridesigns.com

Lil' Irene loves big earrings

Sandra A. Roberts

Sylvia Gbaby Cohen

Lil' Irene

is a

smart girl

with lots of things on her mind.
She doesn't talk much.
Her big earrings speak
most of the time.

Her ears had been pierced
before she was even a year old.

Like the children of Egypt
in the stories Nana told.

These adornments are bold,
bright billboards
that cover her ears.

They express her feelings
and shield her from pressuring peers

She chooses not to wear
heavy pieces.

They drag her down.

She favors statements of
light and love
in shapes that are round.

On some days, she hangs mismatched signs on each side of her head

They remind her to be who she is; not easily led.

With earrings to rock every **outfit** and **occasion**.

She's ready no matter **who**, **what**, **when** or the location.

Until one night,

she did not follow her usual routine

She went to bed before

picking out her clothes and earrings

The next day, while in a hurry
to find something to wear.

Lil' Irene rushed off to school
without her big earring pair!

To make things worse,
she had forgotten it was
Picture Day.

She wanted to leave, but she knew
her mom would make her stay.

She walked around feeling **ugly** and **sad** with her head low.

And no matter how hard she tried, she could not find her **glow.**

She missed her giant earrings filled
with words of love and light.

So she tried to picture them
with her eyes closed nice and tight

She imagined words from **brown faces** of beautiful queens

And her people's great Egyptian history and earrings

Lil' Irene'S attitude and postur suddenly improved.

She felt better about
not wearing her earrings to school.

For Lil' Irene's first time,
no accessories were needed.

She grew **big** inside, because she
finally believed it!

About the Author

Sandra Roberts holds a Bachelor of Arts from Dillard University in New Orleans, Louisiana and a Master of Arts in Teaching from Webster University in Webster Groves, Missouri. With teaching certifications in both Communication Arts and School Library Media, she taught high school English and provided elementary and high school library services for sixteen years.

She currently works as a licensed massage therapist and owner of Books In Our Image, LLC. She lives in Saint Louis, Missouri, where she enjoys spas, pampering, brunches, smoothies, roller-skating, bicycling, movies, libraries and music. Her first two books, "Good Touch Day" and "Come With Me to the Place to Be" are also available on Amazon.

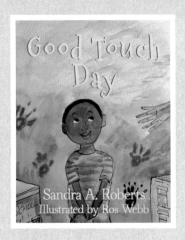

About the Illustrator

Artist, Sylvia "Gbaby" Cohen, founder of Gbaby™, purposes her creations as an apparatus to inspire, encourage, and motivate all who encounter each and every one-of-a-kind piece. Sylvia's Gbaby™ brand officially took root in the early 2000's when Sylvia's teenage daughter, Giovonnie, who was an actress on Nickelodeon's All That, was looking for a handbag to wear to an awards ceremony. Sylvia's creative spirit took hold and she painted her first Gbaby™ handbag. Little did she know it would be the first step into building the brand known today as Gbaby.

Now living in Conyers, Georgia, Sylvia plans to continue to spread the Gbaby™ influence. She is continuing on with her original paintings and mixed media masks. With three licensing deals, her artwork is produced on an array of products. Sylvia has just released her fifth inspirational calendar titled "Aspire, Affirm & Achieve." She has also expanded the reach of the Gbaby brand to include a publishing company, "My Heart on the Line." The company has launched the first book, "The Art of sBusiness; The Business of Art" workbook, and Gbaby's first adult coloring book "Goddess of Nature". Sylvia's books and art are available at gbabyart.com.

Made in the USA
Monee, IL
30 August 2020

40390164R00021